THE ITALIAN CAMPAIGN

LET'S SEE HOW THEY LIKE SOME FRESH BULLETS –

CREATED BY
ALAN HEBDEN
CARLOS EZQUERRA

CREATING A MAJOR CHARACTER

"I'm thinking perhaps an unconventional character, an officer maybe, one who doesn't play by the rules but always gets the job done."

"A scruffy, insubordinate type, you mean? But a guy who knows how to kill?"

"Yeah, that sounds about right. Reckon you can come up with something along those lines?"

"I'll give it a go. Did you say something about going for lunch?"

Thus went the conversation between **Battle Weekly** editor Dave Hunt and myself back in the autumn of 1975, and so was born one of the comic's most iconic characters, the uber-cool Major Eazy.

He came into the world pretty much fully-formed, Bentley sports tourer and all. Only a suitably iconic name was missing, for which his legion of fans can thank the then deputy editor Steve MacManus. It was a completely crazy name when you think about it, but so was the character.

Dave had an artist lined up, some Spanish guy called Carlos Ezquerra who'd been poached from D.C.Thomson. His take on Eazy seemed to border on insanity; an unkempt version of James Coburn on a bad day whose only nod to a uniform was an Afrika Korps forage cap and a leather flying jacket. He was also armed to the teeth and always smoking a cheroot, the most unlikely British officer you would ever hope to meet, but then so was Lawrence of Arabia.

It was love at first sight!

Between us, Carlos and I created this death-dealing whirlwind that tore through Italy and, in subsequent series, through North Africa, Greece, Crete and back to North Africa again, He rarely lost his fabled cool, but on the few occasions that he did, those responsible invariably paid the price.

We shan't see his like again, more's the pity, but hopefully he'll keep popping up when you least expect him.

ALAN HEBDEN

10TH JULY, 1943 — AND BRITISH TROOPS SET FOOT ON THE CONTINENT AGAIN AFTER THREE LONG YEARS. THE INVASION OF SICILY HAS BEGUN!

FOLLOW ME, LADS ... AAARGH!

S'TRUTH! THE MAJOR'S COPPED ONE ALREADY!

It was the worst possible beginning for Sergeant Bert Daly and his men—

YOU'RE IN CHARGE TILL WE GET A REPLACEMENT FOR MAJOR BURNS, SARGE. LEAD US IN!

FIRST WE GOTTA PUT THAT JERRY MACHINE GUN NEST OUT OF ACTION. WE'RE DEAD MEN IF WE DON'T!

TWO OF YOU GIVE US COVERING FIRE. THE REST SPREAD OUT AND BE READY TO CHARGE.

DON'T RECKON WE NEED ANY OFFICER WITH YOU AROUND, SARGE.

MAJOR EAZY

Suddenly —

FOR CRYING OUT LOUD, WHAT'S THAT MANIAC PLAYING AT? THIS AIN'T PICCADILLY CIRCUS!

"YOU'RE CRAZY! ONE MAN AGAINST A KING TIGER —"

NEXT WEEK — EAZY HAS A 'CLOSE SHAVE' WITH DEATH!

MAJOR EAZY

1943. During the invasion of Sicily, Sergeant Daly and his men have found themselves with a remarkable new officer. Major Eazy, an ex-LRDG man, who goes to war in his own car with his own weapons. The strangest officer they've ever known — and the most deadly.

SANTA MARITA AHEAD, MAJOR EAZY. LOOKS LIKE THE JERRIES HAVE ALREADY SCARPERED. SIR? HECK, HE'S ASLEEP AGAIN!

But —

THE ENGLANDERS FORGET WE GERMANS ARE MORE DANGEROUS IN RETREAT THAN IN VICTORY. PREPARE TO FIRE!

IT'S A TRAP!

WHAT THE HECK'S HAPPENING?

Eazy moved like lightning —

S'TRUTH. YOU'RE PICKING THOSE GRENADES OFF IN THE AIR!

JUST CLAY PIGEONS, SERGEANT. NOW FOR THE LIVE ONES IN THE VILLAGE.

MAJOR EAZY, JERRY'S ON HIS WAY BACK — IN FORCE THIS TIME. THEY'LL BE HERE ANY SECOND.

I CAN'T LEAVE YET, DALY — NOT IN THE MIDDLE OF A SHAVE. YOU LOT CLEAR OUT — THAT'S AN ORDER!

ER, PERHAPS IT WOULD BE WISER TO FINISH THIS SHAVE AT ANOTHER TIME, SIGNOR?

YOU'LL FINISH IT NOW, AND HEAVEN HELP YOU IF YOU CUT ME WITH THAT THING. STOP SHAKING!

Meanwhile —

IT DON'T SEEM RIGHT TO LEAVE HIM BACK THERE, SARGE.

THAT'S THE WAY HE WANTED IT — HE'LL NEVER RUN. BUT HE MIGHT HAVE TAKEN ON MORE THAN EVEN HE CAN HANDLE THIS TIME. YOU AND ME ARE GOING BACK!

SO, THE ENGLANDERS HAVE SCUTTLED LIKE SCARED RABBITS. BUT THAT CAR — SURELY THERE CAN'T BE ANY STILL IN THE SHOP?

BARBIERE

DO YOU MIND, I'M IN THE MIDDLE OF A SHAVE!

FOOL! IT IS THE LAST YOU WILL EVER HAVE! KILL HIM!

But Eazy's two holster guns blasted out from behind the shaving cape —

HIMMEL!

AAAGHH!

Just then —

AAAGH!

SHOOTING! IT SOUNDS AS IF WE'RE TOO LATE.

BLAST, STRAIGHT INTO A HERD OF JERRIES!

MORE ENGLANDERS! SEIZE THEM! THEY CAN JOIN THEIR COMRADE IN THE BARBER'S SHOP!

GREAT SCOTT, HE'S BEING SHAVED BY AN SS COLONEL! WHY AREN'T THE JERRIES BLOWING HIM SKY-HIGH?

SILENCE!

NEXT WEEK — MAJOR EAZY RIDDLES MILITARY POLICE WITH LEAD!

"IT'LL BE TOO LATE FOR YOU IF YOU DON'T START SINGING, FRITZ."

NEXT WEEK — EAZY LEADS A MOONLIGHT RAID AGAINST THE GERMANS!

"HE'S LIKE A FLY GOING UP A WALL!"

A REALLY GREAT 'MYSTERY EXTRA' NEXT WEEK! DON'T MISS IT!

NEXT WEEK—EAZY'S MEN ARE CAPTURED BY THE S.S.!

NEXT WEEK — EAZY TEACHES A GREEN OFFICER THE FACTS OF WAR!

I SAID PULL YOURSELF TOGETHER!

UUURGH!

YOU NEARLY KNOCKED HIS HEAD OFF.

I FLAMING WELL WILL NEXT TIME IF HE HAS ANOTHER BOUT OF HYSTERICS LIKE THAT. PUT HIM IN THE CAR. HE CAN COME BACK WITH US AND SEE WHAT SCARED HIM SO MUCH!

WHAT — WHAT HAPPENED? WHERE ARE YOU TAKING ME?

BACK TO THE WAR, KID — AND IF YOU FEEL LIKE RUNNING SCARED AGAIN DON'T FORGET THIS GUN, BECAUSE I'LL SHOOT YOUR LEGS OFF BEFORE YOU'VE GOT TEN YARDS!

OKAY, SHOW ME WHERE IT HAPPENED — AND REMEMBER THIS PISTOL!

IT — IT WAS OVER HERE.

I HOPE THAT YOUNGSTER DON'T THINK HE'S BLUFFING!

THERE.

KEEP AN EYE ON HIM, SERGEANT. I'M GOING TO TAKE A LOOK.

SEEMS CLEAR ENOUGH, BUT I CAN STILL SMELL KRAUT IN THE AREA. BETTER TAKE A SQUINT IN HERE.

HERE GOES!

He emerged a few seconds later —

FIND ANYTHING, SIR?

IN A WAY. BRING THE KID OVER HERE. MAYBE HE SHOULD TAKE A LOOK FOR HIMSELF.

BULLETS FLY FAST WHEN YOU READ "BATTLE" — KEEP YOUR HEAD DOWN!

EAZY HAS MORE THAN ONE WAY TO SKIN A CAT NEXT WEEK!

NEXT WEEK — *EAZY TELLS A WAR CORRESPONDENT HE'S GOING TO DIE!*

In the forefront of the Allied advance into central Italy is the platoon led by Major Eazy, a remarkable officer who wages war in his own dirty style. But the Germans are fighting hard to stem the relentless advance —

THE R.A.F. ARE SENDING OVER A FEW TYPHOONS IN THE NEXT TEN MINUTES, MAJOR EAZY — AND WE NEED 'EM.

FALL BACK BEHIND THESE ROCKS, FAST! THE KRAUTS ARE MAKING IT HOTTER THAN HELL OUT THERE.

HECK, WHO'S THAT LUNATIC OUT THERE.

I DON'T KNOW, BUT HE'LL BE A DEAD ONE IN A FEW MINUTES. GIVE ME SOME COVERING FIRE — I'LL SEE IF I CAN REACH HIM.

MAJOR EAZY

But —

SOME COVERING FIRE! I GUESS IF YOU WANT SOMETHING DONE PROPERLY —

AAAGHH!

— YOU'VE GOT TO DO IT YOURSELF!

NEXT WEEK — MAJOR EAZY . . . TIGER TANK FIGHTER!

At the forefront of the Allied push against the Germans in Italy is Major Eazy — a cool, deadly fighting officer. Now, in the Appenine mountains, he and Sergeant Daly view the scene of an accident --

WHAT'S HAPPENED HERE?

SOMEBODY FORGETTING TO USE THEIR BRAKES BY THE LOOKS OF IT. IT'S A YANK GENERAL'S CAR.

HEY, YOU GUYS — I'M GENERAL HOFFMEYER AN' I NEED TRANSPORT FAST TO REACH THE BRIDGE ACROSS THE LITTORI GORGE. IF THE KRAUTS BLOW IT THEY'LL STOP THE ADVANCE OF A WHOLE DIVISION. WILL YA HELP ME?

SURE. OUT YOU GET FOR THE THREE-STAR GENERAL, DALY — I'LL PICK YOU UP LATER.

THANKS.

MAJOR EAZY

I THOUGHT THAT BRIDGE HAD ALREADY BEEN DESTROYED.

SO DID WE, BUT INTELLIGENCE REPORTED IT STANDING AN HOUR AGO, AN' I GOTTA MAKE SURE!

SAY, SON, YA REALLY KNOW HOW TO HANDLE THIS AUTO, DONTCHA?

I PRACTISE EVERY DAY, GENERAL!

THERE'S GREAT NEWS NEXT WEEK — DON'T MISS YOUR ISSUE!

START COLLECTING YOUR FILE ON THE COMMANDOS NEXT WEEK!

SHOCKS NEXT WEEK WHEN EAZY REFUSES THE VICTORIA CROSS !

JOIN MAJOR EAZY IN ANOTHER DEADLY ADVENTURE NEXT WEEK !

Italy, 1944. In the Appenine mountains north of Rome the Allied invasion force comes up against stubborn German resistance along the Gothic line. As one British officer, the deadly Major Eazy, finds out almost at the cost of his life!

THROUGH THE VILLAGE OF SAN LUIS, AND THEN ACROSS A SMALL PASS. WE'LL GIVE IT A WHIRL. THERE'S GOT TO BE A WAY THROUGH THE GOTHIC LINE SOMEWHERE.

A JUNCTION. CAN YOU SEE WHERE IT LEADS, SIR?

Meanwhile, in San Luis—

WHEW! WE ALMOST COPPED IT THAT TIME, MAJOR EAZY! THE JERRIES HAVE SEALED ANOTHER PASS AND REALLY DUG THEMSELVES IN.

HURRY, MOVE THESE PEASANTS OUT, SHOOT ANY THAT OBJECT! WE'LL SOON SEAL THIS GAP IN OUR DEFENCES!

YOU CAN THANK THEIR C-IN-C, GENERAL VON KESSELRING FOR THAT. HE'S A SECOND ROMMEL IF EVER THERE WAS ONE!

ENGLANDERS... KILL THEM!

DAMN — JUST OUR LUCK TO CRASH ONE OF THE SS'S TEA PARTIES —

MAJOR EAZY

TAKE THE WHEEL... I'M GOING TO NEED BOTH HANDS FOR THIS!

WHAT A TIME TO CHANGE DRIVERS!

ARGH!

ARGH!

MAJOR!

GET THEM, MULLER... YOU'RE THE BEST GRENADE THROWER IN THE COMPANY!

JAWOHL, HERR OBERST! AT THIS RANGE I CANNOT MISS!

MORE HARD-HITTING ACTION WITH MAJOR EAZY IN NEXT WEEK'S ISSUE!

NEVER WAKE A PROFESSIONAL SUDDENLY, ESPECIALLY IF HIS NAME IS...

MAJOR EAZY

A GIRL TRIES TO BLOW UP MAJOR EAZY NEXT WEEK! DON'T MISS IT!

MORE DEADLY ACTION WITH THE WAR'S TOUGHEST SOLDIER NEXT WEEK !

EVER WANTED TO OWN A 'SPITFIRE'? SEE BATTLE STATIONS FOR DETAILS!

MAJOR EAZY RETURNS WITH MORE KILL-OR-BE-KILLED ACTION NEXT WEEK !

NEXT WEEK — THE KILLING COMES EASY WHEN EAZY'S AMBUSHED IN A SLAUGHTERHOUSE !

NEXT WEEK – SOMEONE IS OUT TO KILL EAZY – AND IT COULD BE ANY OF A HUNDRED OLD ENEMIES !

JOIN THE WAR'S TOUGHEST FIGHTING SOLDIER FOR MORE TOUGH ACTION NEXT WEEK !

A HAIR-RAISING CHASE IN A HEARSE FOR MAJOR EAZY NEXT WEEK !

THIS IS THE LOT, SIR. THREE OF 'EM.

WHO GAVE THE ORDERS FOR THE MASSACRE? TELL ME, FRITZ—AND TELL ME QUICKLY, BECAUSE I'M NOT GOING TO WAIT FOR AN ANSWER!

NEIN! I WILL KILL YOU RATHER THAN TELL YOU—

Suddenly, Eazy spotted a tiny grenade in the Nazi's hand—

WRONG ANSWER, FRITZ—AND A WRONG MOVE!

AAAARGH!

I'LL TRY AGAIN. WHO GAV THE ORDERS FOR THIS?

NEIN, NEIN—IT WAS GRUPPEN-FUHRER KLAUST. HE LEFT IN HIS CAR WITH AN ESCORT TEN MINUTES AGO, HEADING FOR PADUA.

And—

THAT'LL DO. I DON'T THINK WE NEED TO BOTHER WITH YOU TWO ANY LONGER. TAKE 'EM AWAY.

THIS IS A REAL ROUGH RIDE THESE TWO ARE LUCKY TO BE ALIVE. I'VE NEVER SEEN EAZY IN SUCH A DARK MOOD.

THE KILLERS—WHY DON'T YOU SLAUGHTER 'EM NOW, MAJOR?

YOU DON'T MURDER NAZI ANIMALS. YOU EXTER-MINATE THEM — AFTER THEIR TRIAL!

YOU CAN'T GO AFTER KLAUST ALONE, SIR!

BETTER I SHOULD, DALY. BESIDES, THE CAR'LL GO FASTER WITHOUT A PASSENGER AND I'VE GOT A LOT OF CATCHING UP TO DO.

The miles flashed by, until—

DUST CLOUD BEYOND THAT VILLAGE. IT'S GOTTA BE HIM.

But—

SAPRISTI!

BLAST!

WHAT ARE YOU..? AARH!

BORROWING YOUR HEARSE, PAL.

STAND READY FOR GREAT NEWS IN NEXT WEEK'S ISSUE, LADS !

THE NAME'S MAJOR LEICHT, ENGLANDER. THIS END OF THE BRIDGE EXPLODES IN THIRTY SECONDS. YOU DESERVE THE CHANCE TO GET AWAY.

THANKS, LEICHT... I'LL REMEMBER THIS. EAZY'S THE NAME... MAJOR EAZY!

WHAT THE HELL'S GOING ON?

HOLD THAT TIN CAN. THE FAR END OF THE BRIDGE IS GOING UP, COURTESY OF ONE MAJOR LEICHT!

Two seconds later —

YE GODS!

DON'T SAY I DIDN'T WARN YOU.

A week later —

A WHOLE WEEK WASTED BEFORE THEY COULD BUILD A PONTOON BRIDGE ACROSS THE RIVER THAT WOULDN'T GET WASHED AWAY BY THE FLOOD TIDE. THAT JERRY MAJOR SURE THREW A SPANNER IN OUR WORKS.

AND GAVE THEM TIME TO RE-ORGANISE THEIR DEFENCES FURTHER BACK. BUT WE'RE ON THE MOVE NOW.

Soon —

WHAT'S THE HOLD UP? YOU REALISE THAT HALF A KRAUT BRIGADE'S SLIPPING AWAY NORTH WHILE YOU HANG ABOUT HERE?

I KNOW THAT, SIR... BUT THERE'S A BUNCH OF S.S. TROOPS IN THAT SCHOOL WITH THE KIDS AS HOSTAGES. THEY'VE THREATENED TO KILL THE LOT IF WE ADVANCE!

Then a familiar car arrived —

AT LEAST I'LL DROP ONE OF THE ...HEY!

LEAVE HIM BE! I'VE GOT A FEELING THIS IS THE ONLY WAY TO SAVE THOSE KIDS.

LET THEM GO! THERE'LL BE NO WAR ON CHILDREN WHILE I'M HERE!

BUT...BUT, HERR MAJOR LEICHT, THE BRITISCHERS WILL TRAP THE REST OF THE BRIGADE!

AS YOU SEEM UNABLE TO FIGHT LIKE SOLDIERS YOU'D BETTER GO WITH THEM BEFORE I REALLY LOSE MY TEMPER! I'LL HOLD UP THE ENGLANDERS LONG ENOUGH MYSELF IF I HAVE TO. GET OUT!

WHAT HAPPENED? WHY DID THEY LET THE KIDS GO?

BECAUSE THERE'S A MAN WORTH A HUNDRED S.S. TROOPS OVER THERE NOW. CAREFUL HOW YOU GO, CAPTAIN. TAKING HIM ISN'T GOING TO BE AS EASY AS YOU THINK.

FOUR NEW STORIES START IN NEXT WEEK'S SPECIAL ISSUE — DON'T MISS IT!

RIVERS OF BLOOD WHEN EAZY VISITS VENICE NEXT WEEK !

FIND OUT WHY EAZY SAVES GERMANS FROM HANGING NEXT WEEK !

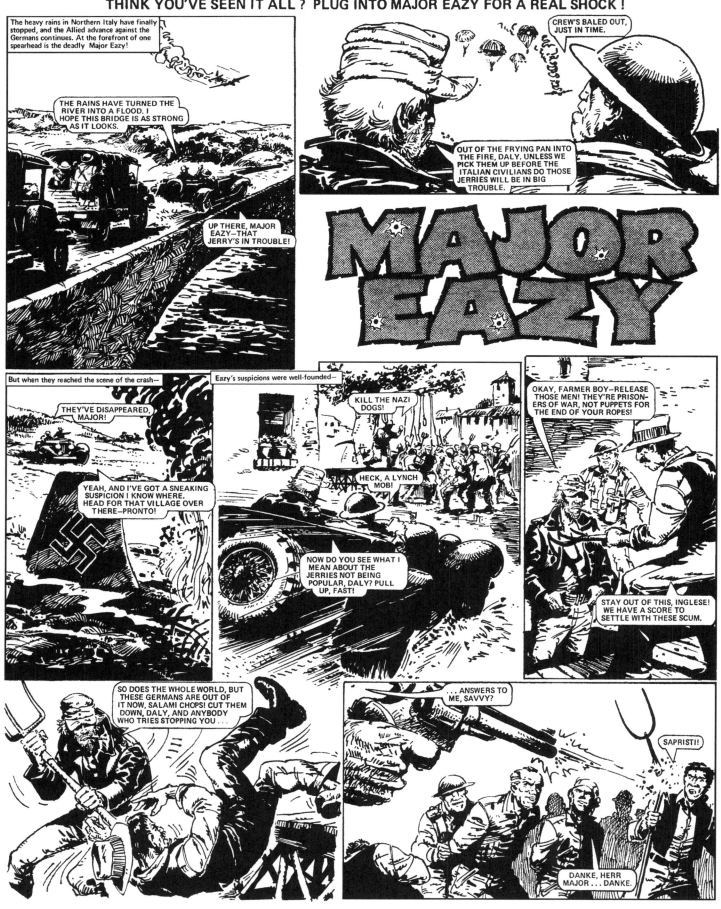

THE FINAL PART OF YOUR DEADLY MACHINE GUN POSTER NEXT ISSUE !

THE GREAT CHASE IS ON — EAZY STYLE — NEXT WEEK !

SPARKS FLY WHEN EAZY MEETS AN OLD MATE FROM THE L.R.D.G. NEXT WEEK !

JOIN THE WAR'S DEADLIEST SOLDIER FOR MORE ACTION NEXT WEEK !

And—

IT'S QUITE SIMPLE, MAJOR—SOME OF THE CIVILIANS' SUPPLIES ARE FINDING THEIR WAY INTO GERMAN HANDS, AND WE AIN'T IN BUSINESS TO FEED THE KRAUTS. NO SUPPLIES TO THE CIVILIANS SO NO SUPPLIES GET TO THE KRAUTS. SIMPLE ... HUH?

PLAIN SUICIDAL, COLONEL! THE CIVILIANS'LL STARVE LONG BEFORE THE KRAUTS—IF THEY DON'T TURN AGAINST US FIRST.

THAT'S TOUGH! SERVE 'EM RIGHT FOR PASSING THE GOODS ON TO THE ENEMY IN THE FIRST PLACE.

THIS'LL MEAN BIG TROUBLE FOR ALL OF US, COLONEL!

IT'LL MEAN BIG TROUBLE FOR YOU IF YOU AIN'T GONE FROM HERE IN TEN SECONDS – SIR!

I'VE HAD ALL THE LIP I'M GONNA TAKE FROM YOU. TURN THE CAR ROUND, DALY—AND LET'S GET AWAY FROM HERE—PRONTO!

YUURGH!

The following morning the British captured a small town from the Germans—

JUST THIS BLOKE INSIDE, SIR. OH, AND A WHOLE LOT OF UNIFORMS. MUST HAVE BEEN A CLOTHING STORE.

UNIFORMS, EH? THAT COULD BE INTERESTING. SPEAK ENGLISH, FRITZ?

A LITTLE, ENGLANDER—BUT YOU WILL LEARN NOTHING FROM ME.

DON'T BLOW A FUSE, FRIEND. THE ONLY INFORMATION I WANT FROM YOU IS TO KNOW IF YOU'D BE INTERESTED IN A LITTLE PROPOSITION I'VE GOT IN MIND.

TELL ME MORE, ENGLANDER.

I DON'T LIKE THIS. WHAT'S THE MAJOR UP TO NOW?

I DON'T GET IT, MR. EAZY. WHAT ARE WE ALL CHANGING INTO JERRY UNIFORMS FOR?

YOU'LL FIND OUT, SERGEANT. LET'S JUST SAY THAT A CERTAIN STUBBORN YANK COLONEL'S IN FOR A NASTY SHOCK.

Back at the American supply depot—

OKAY, FRITZ, YOU'RE IN CHARGE FROM HERE ON. DO WHAT WE AGREED AND I'LL KEEP MY PART OF THE BARGAIN.

I BELIEVE YOU WILL, HERR EAZY. LEAVE IT TO ME— I SHALL ENJOY THIS.

OKAY, WHAT'S YA— HOLY DODGERS, KRAUTS!

PRECISELY, AMERIKANER SCUM. KINDLY STEP ON TO THE RUNNING BOARD AND REMAIN QUITE SILENT—

NICELY SAID, FRITZ!

A CRACK GERMAN SNIPER IS ORDERED TO RUB OUT EAZY NEXT WEEK !

Later, at Brigade H.Q. —

Soon —

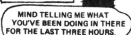

A few hours later —

That night —

NEXT WEEK – A RACE TO SAVE LIVES IN A TUNNEL OF DEATH !

THE NEWS IS BIG IN NEXT WEEK'S ISSUE ! DON'T MISS IT !

EAZY RUMBLES A GERMAN AGENT OPERATING IN THE DESERT NEXT WEEK !

NEXT WEEK — MASSACRE IN THE DESERT !

CAN EAZY SURVIVE? DON'T MISS PART TWO OF THIS GREAT STORY!

Cast loose in the desert by a fanatical sheik, without water, Major Eazy of the Long Range Desert Group is closer to death than he has ever been after miles of walking under the pitiless sun.

MUST KEEP GOING. . .MUSTN'T STOP. . .NEVER GET GOING AGAIN IF I DO.

Eazy never saw the steeply sloping hillside.

WHAT THE. . . AAARRGH !

He survived the fall. . .but only just.

SO THIS IS IT, PAL. A MESSY WAY TO DIE, BUT I SUPPOSE MOST OF 'EM ARE. PITY, THOUGH. I'D HAVE GIVEN IT ALL UP ANYWAY FOR TEN SECONDS ALONE WITH THAT SHEIK. A REAL PITY.

Hours passed then, suddenly, the blazing sun was blotted from his view —

WHAT THE – ? TEWFIK ?

BE STILL AND DON'T SPEAK, EFFENDI. HOW YOU CAME THIS FAR WITHOUT WATER NO-ONE WILL EVER KNOW. ONLY A MAN WITH A BURNING DESIRE TO LIVE COULD HAVE KEPT GOING.

REVENGE, TEWFIK. . . I LIVED FOR REVENGE ON THAT SHEIK.

THEN THE TIME WILL SURELY COME, BUT NOT NOW. THEY WILL SEND YOU BACK TO HOSPITAL IN CAIRO.

MAJOR EAZY

Two weeks later —

WELCOME TO THE RITZ, TEWFIK. YOU'RE LOOKING GRIM.

BAD NEWS, EFFENDI. I HEAR FROM HEADQUARTERS THAT THE ONE WHO DID THIS TO YOU IS BEING TREATED LIKE AN ALLY. YOUR GENERALS SEEK HIS HELP AGAINST THE GERMANS.

HEY, WHERE ARE YOU GOING ? NOBODY SAID YOU COULD GET OUT OF BED !

ANYBODY TRIES KEEPING ME IN ONE NOW'S GOING TO END UP IN ONE THEMSELVES. OUT OF THE WAY. I'VE GOT THINGS TO DO !

IT IS THE WILL OF ALLAH !

At Headquarters —

At the airport —

EAZY AND ROMMEL COOK UP A PLAN TO DEAL WITH THE SHEIK NEXT WEEK !

JOIN THE DESERT WAR'S COOLEST SOLDIER FOR MORE ACTION NEXT WEEK !

BUT EVEN EAZY CAN BE SHOCKED — SEE NEXT WEEK !

JOIN MAJOR EAZY FOR MORE SHOCKS AND SURPRISES NEXT WEEK !

TROUBLE FOR EAZY WHEN HE MEETS THE FOREIGN LEGION NEXT WEEK !

MORE ACTION YOU NEVER EVEN DREAMED OF NEXT WEEK !

IS THIS THE END FOR EAZY ? FIND OUT NEXT ISSUE !

A BULLET FROM NOWHERE SAVES EAZY'S LIFE!

NEXT WEEK – EAZY IS FORCED TO TAKE ON A DESK JOB !

IF EAZY WAS YOUR TEACHER YOU'D HAVE A WHALE OF A TIME !

JOIN EAZY FOR MORE DEVASTATING ACTION NEXT ISSUE !

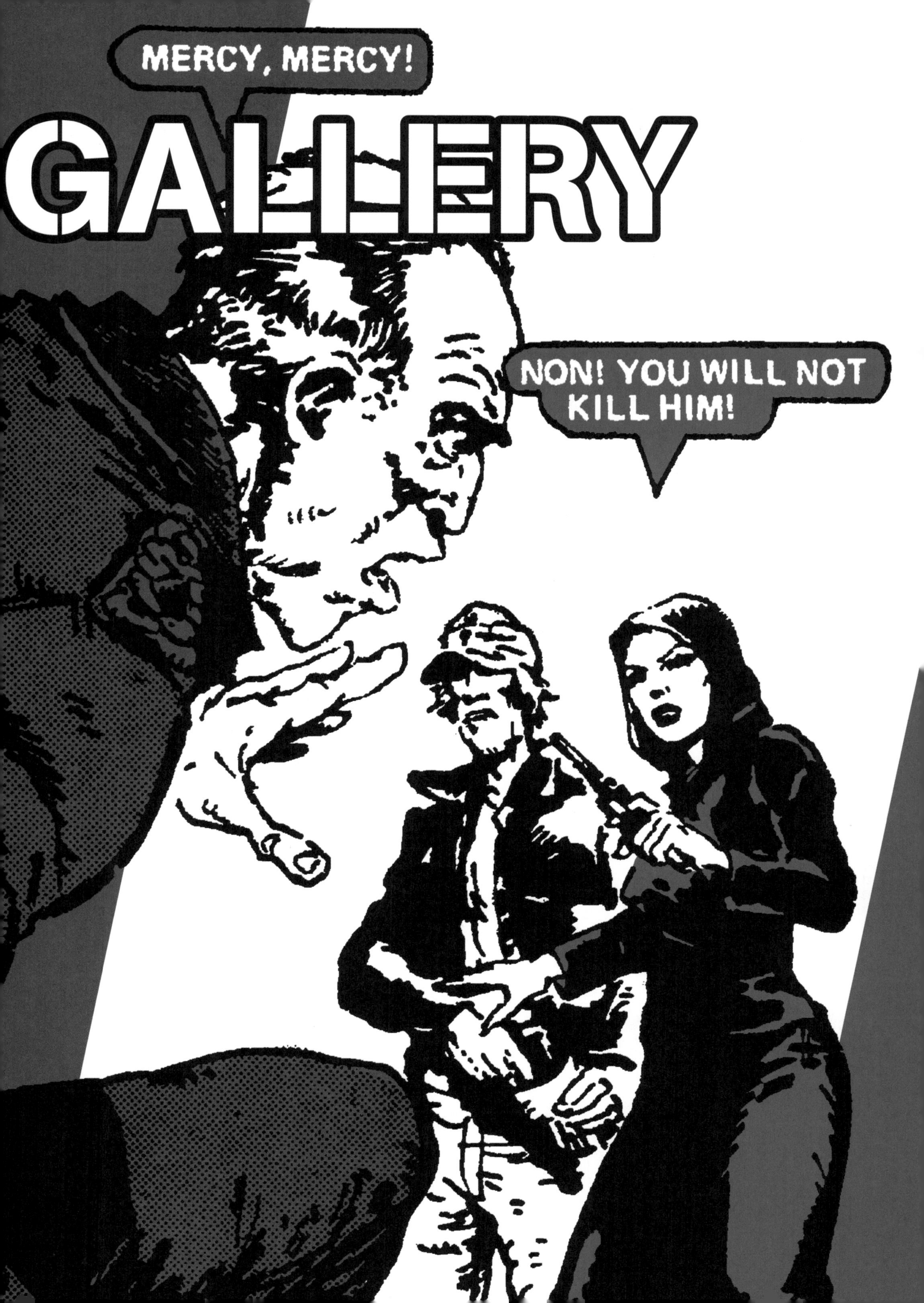
MERCY, MERCY!
GALLERY
NON! YOU WILL NOT KILL HIM!

THE PAPER WITH ALL-ACTION WAR STORIES

BATTLE
PICTURE WEEKLY

7 FEBRUARY, 1976 EVERY THURSDAY

7p

EAZY BLASTS A YANK PLANE !

See dramatic story inside !

PLUS DESTROYER IN GREAT SEA ACTION

SPY THRILLS with MIKE NELSON

ANOTHER EXCITING **MYSTERY EXTRA** IN THIS ISSUE!

07 February 1976

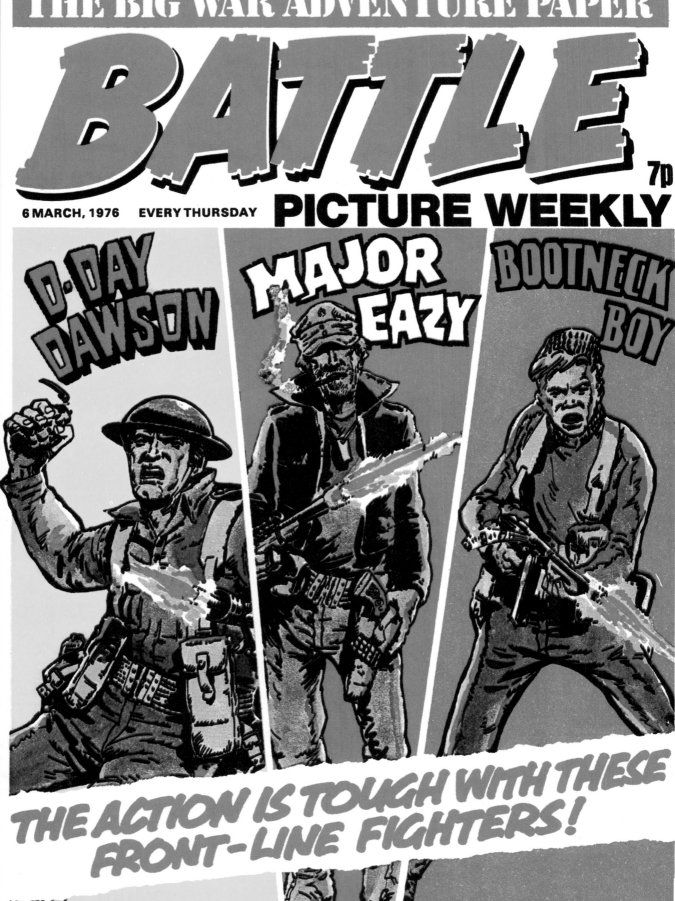

06 March 1976

15 May 1976

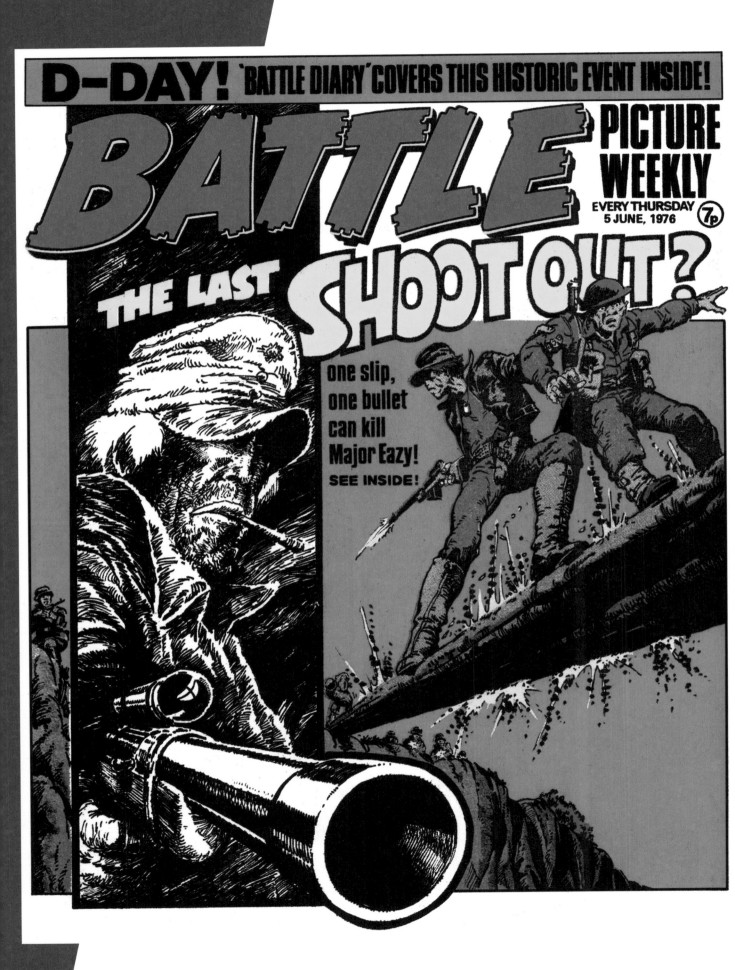

16 October 1976